No Space to Waste

Written by Yvonne Morrison
Illustrated by John Bennett

My name is Vineeta. I live in New Delhi. It is a very busy city with about 14,000,000 people. Some people say that there are too many people in India. Families are growing larger. Cities are becoming more overcrowded. How will people have enough space to live?

www.heinemannlibrary.co.uk
Visit our website to find out more information about Heinemann Library books.

To order:
Phone +44 (0) 1865 888066
Fax +44 (0) 1865 314091
Visit www.heinemannlibrary.co.uk

Heinemann Library is an imprint of **Capstone Global Library Limited**, a company incorporated in England and Wales having its registered office at 7 Pilgrim Street, London, EC4V 6LB – Registered company number: 6695582

First published by Weldon Owen Education Inc. in 2008
First published in hardback in the United Kingdom in 2009

Written by Yvonne Morrison
Edited by Briony Hill
Designed by Matthew Alexander
Original illustrations © Weldon Owen Education Inc. 2008
Illustrated by John Bennett
Picture research by Jamshed Mistry
Originated by Weldon Owen Education Inc.

Printed in China through Colorcraft Ltd., Hong Kong

Acknowledgements
We would like to thank the following for permission to reproduce photographs: Big Stock Photo (crowd, background, pp. 22–23); Briony Hill (Mexican police officer, p. 20); CIESIN: Reprinted from The World: Population Density, 2000. Copyright 2005 Center for International Earth Science Information Network (CIESIN), Columbia University; and Centro Internacional de Agricultura Tropical (CIAT). Gridded Population of the World Version 3 (GPWv3). Palisades, NY: Socioeconomic Data and Applications Center (SEDAC), CIESIN, Columbia University. Available at http://sedac.ciesin.columbia.edu/gpw (map, p. 15); Directorate of Family Welfare, India (poster, p. 19); Getty Images (cover; pp. 14–15; Brazilian protestors, p. 21); Ingram Image Library (Rome, background, pp. 20–21); iStockPhoto.com (Paris traffic, p. 20); Jennifer and Brian Lupton (students, pp. 22–23); Photolibrary ('thinking cap' hat, all pages; pp. 2–3; p. 18; Nigerian school children, p. 21; p. 24); © SCPhotos/Alamy (p. 18); Tranz: Corbis (p. 1; pp. 16–17; overcrowded bus, p. 19; Cairo subway, p. 20); Reuters (Filipinos, p. 21)

ISBN 978-0-431179-62-9 (hardback)
13 12 11 10 09
10 9 8 7 6 5 4 3 2 1

British Library Cataloguing in Publication Data
Morrison, Yvonne, 1972-
No space to waste: population. – (Worldscapes)
304.6'2-dc22
A full catalogue record for this book is available from the British Library.

Contents

Look for the **Thinking Cap**.
When you see this picture, you will find a problem to think about and write about.

Crowded out

Full house

Vijay was **frustrated**. His sister Riya's wedding would take place tomorrow. Family from all over India had come to stay. Aunts, uncles and cousins filled every room. Vijay lived with his parents, grandparents, brother and three sisters in a small house. He was used to noise and crowds, but this was ridiculous!

frustrated feeling helpless and discouraged

Vijay wanted to read the book Uncle Ashok had brought him, but his younger brother and cousins were playing loudly in the living room. Vijay went into another room. His sisters and their friends were chatting loudly about the wedding there.

'No boys allowed!' they squealed and chased him into the yard. Outside, Vijay's father and uncles were putting up the wedding **mandapa**, shouting and laughing noisily. Vijay was in the way. He sighed and walked back inside, into the kitchen.

Weddings are very special occasions in India. Many Indian weddings take place outdoors, at the bride's home.

mandapa special canopy often used in a Hindu wedding

Hot, crowded streets

Vijay's mother and aunts were cooking wedding food. 'Vijay!' said his mother. 'Your Auntie Meena called to say that your wedding suit is nearly ready. Lata will take you to get it.'

Vijay groaned. A trip across town would mean even more crowds. Vijay and his sister Lata waited at the bus stop. When the bus arrived, it was already full. They squeezed into the crowd of people. The bus moved slowly along the busy streets.

Cars, trucks, ox carts and bicycles pushed for space, their drivers yelling and honking.

'No space to waste!' Lata said with a laugh.

She was used to the busy city streets. They were usually packed. The sound of car horns filled the air from morning till night.

Traffic chaos

Soon the bus began to go even more slowly than usual. Vijay wondered why. He squeezed through the crowd to look out the front window. A cow was wandering along the side of the road. The traffic had slowed to a crawl. Suddenly, the cow wandered onto the road.

A man pulling a cart overloaded with bananas turned quickly to avoid it, and his load spilled.

The bus jerked to a stop. Some people on the footpath rushed over to help.

Lata grabbed Vijay's hand and dragged him off the bus.

She whistled to a driver in a passing **rickshaw**, and they piled into the back. The rickshaw driver pedalled around the cart and the bananas. They were moving at last!

Cows are special to Hindu people. Many Hindus take care never to harm a cow.

rickshaw three-wheeled vehicle, usually a cycle, that carries passengers

Auntie Meena's place

Finally, Vijay and Lata reached Auntie Meena's apartment. They were tired and thirsty. Meena led the children into the living room, where **pakoras** and cool mango drinks were waiting for them. Some of Vijay's cousins were there, crowded around the TV, watching a movie. Meena opened a pot of pins.

'I need to measure you,' Meena said to Vijay. Then she unrolled a measuring tape.

'Don't look,' Vijay told his cousins. His cousin Jasmine giggled. Meena measured Vijay's arms and legs as he stood uncomfortably. Dance music blared from the TV. When Auntie Meena had finished measuring Vijay, he sat down to watch the movie. Soon the sound of Meena's sewing machine added to the noise.

pakora crispy vegetable fritter

Apartments are common in Indian cities. There is not enough space for many people to have houses.

Home and away

The suit was ready. Vijay and Lata said goodbye to their cousins, and Meena hurried them into a taxi. 'It's better than a bus,' she said. 'You don't want to wrinkle the suit!'

The taxi driver moved through the busy streets, honking his horn.

Suddenly, they came to a stop. A **tuk-tuk** had broken down in the middle lane. Their driver got out of the taxi and helped the car's owner push it to the side of the road. Then they were on their way again.

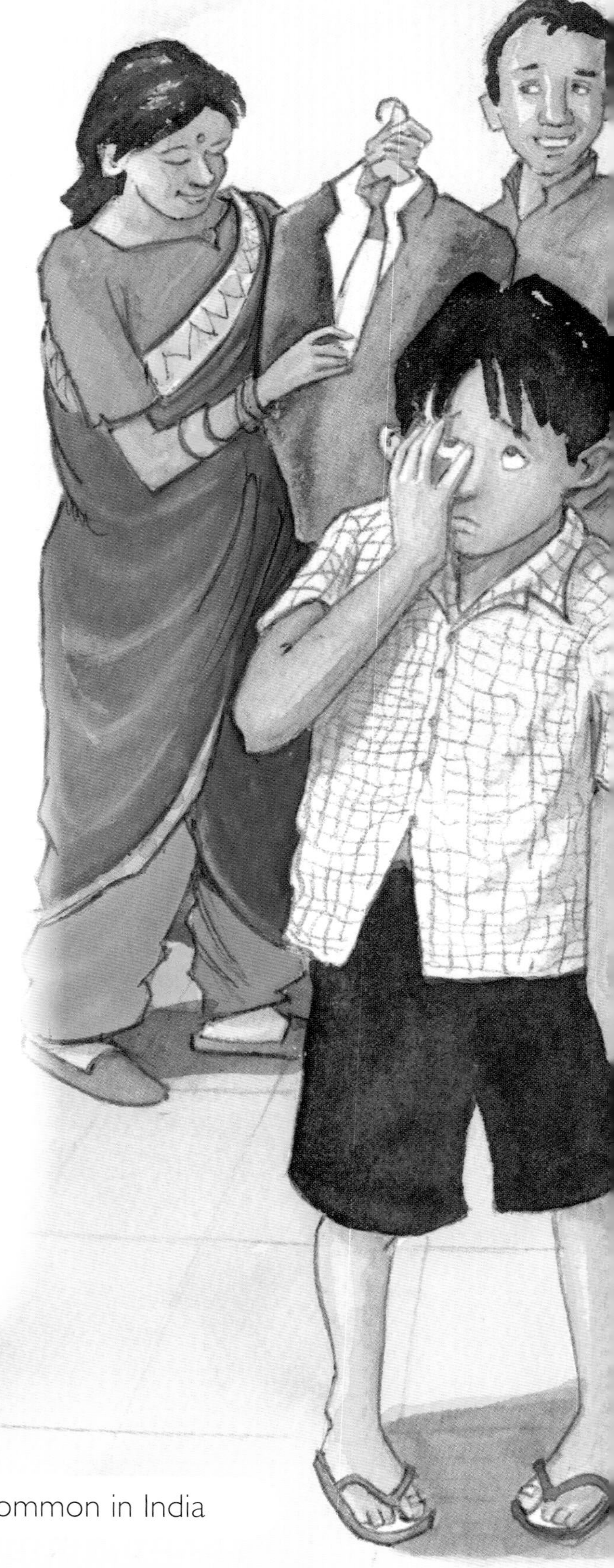

tuk-tuk type of three-wheeled car common in India

Put on your thinking cap

Write down your thoughts so that you can talk about these questions with a classmate.

1. On average, there are about a third more people per square kilometre in India as in the United Kingdom. How do you think this makes a difference to life in the two countries?
2. Imagine you grew up in India, surrounded by lots of people. If you then moved to the United Kingdom, how do you think you would feel? What would you like? What would you find hard?

At last, they arrived home. Vijay thrust the suit at his mother. 'There you go,' he said. His mother unzipped the wrapper and inspected the outfit.

'Oh dear,' she said. 'Meena forgot the waistcoat. You'll just have to go back!'

Vijay groaned. 'I don't believe it!'

What's the issue?

Has anyone ever told you that you are 'one in a million'? Actually, you are one in about six-and-a-half billion! That is how many people live on planet Earth right now, and the number is growing. Babies are being born at a faster rate than people are dying, so the world's **population** is increasing. But the size of Earth is not increasing. Many places around the world are becoming crowded. People need to find ways to be sure that everyone has enough food, space and a good quality of life.

In 2000, India's population reached one billion. The billionth citizen was born in a hospital in New Delhi.

population the number of people living in an area

Where people live

People are not spread evenly over Earth. The map below shows where people live. The darker areas have more people. The lighter areas have fewer people. China and India have the most people. The United States has the third-largest population, but it has a lot of space in which people can live.

World population map

Key

Average number of people per square kilometre (0.4 square mile)

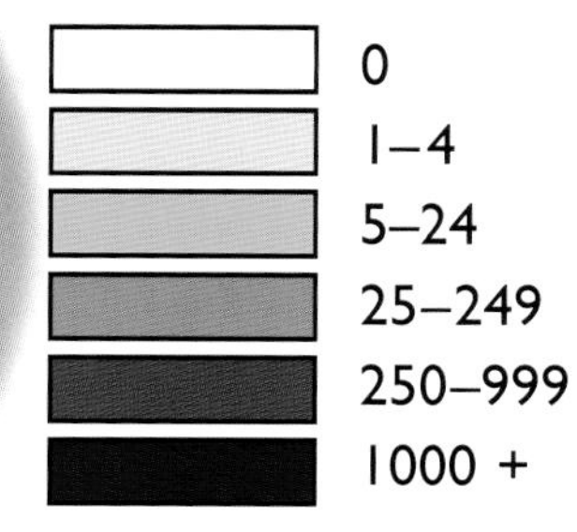

Scientists believe that Earth's population will be almost 10 billion by the year 2050.

Resources hit hard

What would happen if your class got a new student every day, but your classroom stayed the same size? For the first few days, you would be able to fit the new students in, but soon the class would run out of desks, chairs and other **resources**. There wouldn't be enough room to move!

In some countries, this is what is happening. The population is getting so large that there are not enough resources to go around. People do not have enough space to live comfortably. In India, for example, the population increases each year by about the same number of people as the entire population of New York state – about 19,000,000 people!

Crowded Varanasi city lies on the River Ganges.

The world's resources are not spread evenly. About 20 per cent of the population uses about 80 per cent of the world's paper, steel and timber.

resource something that humans use, such as water, timber or oil

The cutting down of forests is a problem in many countries. Without strictly enforced laws, entire forests are disappearing.

Put on your thinking cap

Two resources that people use are farmland and oil. With growing populations, more and more resources are needed and are being used. Write down your thoughts, then talk to a classmate.

1. In India and many other countries, forests are being cut down to create more farmland. How do you think this affects the environment and wild animals, such as tigers?
2. The world's available supplies of oil are running low. Do you know of any problems that this is causing? What problems might it cause in the future?

Bengal tigers are losing their homes and food supply.

A population explosion

More than one billion people live in India. It has one of the fastest-growing populations in the world. In the 1950s, the Indian government became worried that the population was getting too large. The government started a **campaign** to convince couples to have fewer children. However, in India, as in some other countries, it has been a tradition for sons to carry on a family business and name. Parents often kept having babies until they had two boys.

Today, in the southern state of Kerala, there is a focus on educating women. About 85 per cent of women there can read and write, compared with about 50 per cent in the rest of India. Some women are choosing to have fewer children because of their careers.

Female scientists are becoming more common in India.

campaign series of actions organised over a period of time in order to achieve or win something

This poster says, 'Why only a boy? Are these not girls?' It shows women in professional jobs. It encourages parents to be happy with daughters and not to keep trying to have sons.

Population problems

- About 40 per cent of India's population is under the age of 15. If all these young people grow up to have children, the population will get even larger.
- Expanding cities are causing much of India's forests to disappear and pollution to increase. Animals such as the rhinoceros, tiger and Asian elephant are in danger of losing their habitats.
- In many villages in India, women have to walk kilometres each day to collect water. Often this water is polluted.
- Trains and buses are very crowded in India. People often cling dangerously to the outside of vehicles!

India covers only about $2\frac{1}{2}$ per cent of Earth's area, but it has 16 per cent of its people.

Crowds around the world

Take the train

CAIRO, EGYPT – A new railway system has opened recently. Cairo is one of the most traffic-crowded cities in the world. It is hoped that people will take a train instead of a car.

Four times as large

MEXICO CITY, MEXICO – The capital's population is three times larger than it was in 1950, and it is growing quickly. City officials say they do not have enough police officers, firefighters or doctors to make sure everyone is safe.

Traffic tangle

PARIS, FRANCE – A man stuck in a two-hour traffic jam became so angry that he left his car and walked home. His deserted car caused even more delays, because it blocked a lane.

More classrooms

NIGERIA – The government has built 3,000 new classrooms in an attempt to reduce class overcrowding. The next step is to train more teachers and to buy more books and other equipment.

Crime level rises

MANILA, PHILIPPINES – Crime rates have increased as people turn to stealing to try to make a better life for themselves. Many people are living in crowded conditions and do not have enough money to relocate.

Save the trees

BRAZIL – Protesters in Brazil are worried that a nature reserve might be cleared in order to make way for more farmland. The farmers say that they need the land to produce more food for Brazil's growing population.

What's your opinion?

There are more people on Earth now than at any time in the past. This has led to overcrowding, pollution and other problems. Many people do not have enough food, clean water or other resources. However, some people say that there are enough resources on Earth for everyone. They just need to be spread out more fairly. People in wealthy countries need to stop wasting resources.

- Do you think problems such as pollution and hunger are caused by too many people or by other issues?
- What do you think will happen in the future if the human population keeps increasing?

I think the size of Earth's population is causing problems. However, everyone has a right to live. If wealthy people share their resources, everyone will have enough and there will be less waste and pollution.

There may be enough resources for today's population, but if the population keeps increasing, we will run out. No amount of sharing will be enough. We need to focus on the problem now before it is too late.
There are more than twice as many people alive today as in 1960. There are more than six times as many people as in 1800.
Lots of countries have population problems. It's not only those with too many people. Countries with decreasing populations also suffer. Maybe governments in countries that aren't crowded should invite more people from crowded countries to live there.

Think tank

1. Do you think the population of Earth can go on increasing forever? Why or why not?

2. Traffic jams are one of the problems caused by overcrowding. What could people do to prevent traffic jams?

Do your own research at the library, on the Internet, or with a parent or teacher to find out more about population issues around the world and how people are working together to solve these problems.

Glossary

campaign series of actions organised over a period of time in order to achieve or win something

frustrated feeling helpless and discouraged

mandapa special canopy often used in a Hindu wedding

pakora crispy vegetable fritter

population the number of people living in an area

resource something that humans use, such as water, timber or oil

rickshaw three-wheeled vehicle, usually a cycle, that carries passengers

tuk-tuk type of three-wheeled car common in India

Index